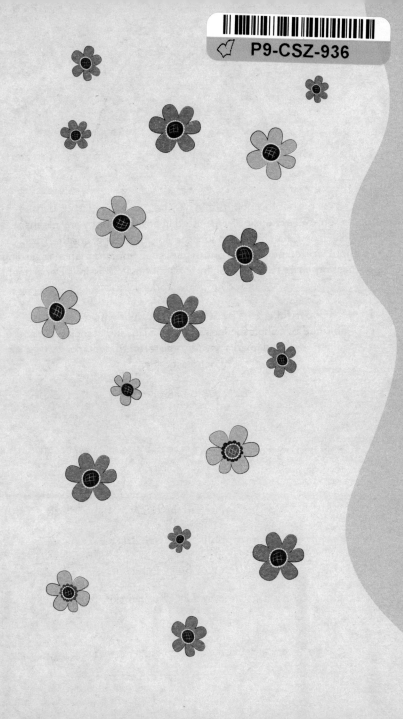

Copyright © 2013 by Scholastic Inc. All rights reserved.
Published by Scholastic Inc. SCHOLASTIC and associated logos
are trademarks and/or registered trademarks
of Scholastic Inc.

ISBN 978-0-545-61960-8

12 11 10 9 8 7 6 5 4 3   17 18 19/0

Printed in the U.S.A.   40

First printing, January 2014

Illustrated by Stacy Peterson

Designed by Janet Kusmierski

BFF

Quizzes, Activities & Tips!

Boredom Busters
Activities
to Share

BY MEGAN FAULKNER

SCHOLASTIC INC.

Table of Contents

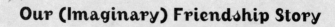

Our (Imaginary) Friendship Story

of _____ and _____

Instructions: Do not show your friend this page. Request answers to the missing words below and fill in the blanks. Read aloud when finished.

I remember the day we met like it was yesterday. It

was a(n) _____ day at the _____ in
           adjective   place

_____. You were in the middle of _____,
country   adverb/verb

when I tapped you _____ on the _____
                   adverb   body part

and said, "Excuse me, do you have any _____?"
                                    adjective/plural noun

You replied, "_____! It just so happens I have
            exclamation

_____." I was impressed by your _____,
number/previous plural noun   adjective/noun

and you remarked that you had never seen a(n)

_____ quite like mine. It was then that
adjective/noun

we realized we both loved _____. We clasped
                         noun

_____, looked to the _____, and
plural noun   noun

shouted _____! And have been best friends
         exclamation

ever since.

The End

BREAKING NEWS:
The REAL Story of How We Met

Best friends since _____ , _____ and
<small>year you met</small>   <small>your full name</small>

_____ met for the first time in _____.
<small>your friend's full name</small>   <small>place where you met</small>

"The minute I saw _____," said _____,
<small>your friend's name</small>   <small>your last name</small>

"I immediately thought, _____."
<small>whatever you thought</small>

_____ laughs. "That's so funny, because I was
<small>your friend's last name</small>

thinking, _____!"
<small>whatever your friend was thinking</small>

And the rest, as they say, is history.

TO BE CONTINUED . . .

Add photos here.

_____
name

How We're Different

What are some of the things that make each of you unique?

Looks

_____

_____

_____

Talents

_____

_____

_____

Hobbies

_____

_____

_____

Family

_____

_____

_____

Likes

_____

_____

_____

Dislikes

_____

_____

_____

How We're Different

What are some of the things that make each of you unique?

Looks

_____

_____

_____

_____

Hobbies

_____

_____

_____

_____

Likes

_____

_____

_____

_____

Talents

_____

_____

_____

_____

Family

_____

_____

_____

_____

Dislikes

_____

_____

_____

_____

Why We Click

What are some of the things that tie you and your BFF together?

1. We both love talking about _Dogs_

2. We always laugh when _We play_

3. Neither of us like _clowns_

4. Both of us really want to _go on a trip together_

5. On weekends, we can't wait to _see each other_

6. When we grow up, we both want to _take care of animals_

7. We always know when the other is down because _thest face expression_

8. Both of us hate _some people_

9. We never get tired of _playing_

10. We would both rather die than _eatin some thing bad_

Quiz: Test Your BFF Intuition

Do you know what your BFF is thinking before she tells you? Do you finish each other's sentences? This quiz will show how in sync you are with each other.

Instructions: Decide who will be Friend A and who will be Friend B. Friend A privately answers her questions **as she thinks** Friend B would answer them.

When finished, pass the questions to Friend B to verify. Add up how many matches you have. Repeat the process for Friend A.

QUESTIONS FOR FRIEND A

1. The first thing I do when I get home from school is
   _____

2. If I don't respond to your text, I am probably _____
   _____

3. I'm always happy to go shopping for _____
   _____

4. If I'm crying, it's most likely because _____
   _____

5. I will always smile if you bring me _____

6. When I get to choose what we have for dinner, my first choice is _____, with _____ for dessert.

7. The thing that frustrates me the most is _____
   _____

8. If I were stranded on a desert island and could take one thing from my bedroom it would be _____ _____

9. The easiest way to get me to laugh is _____ _____

10. I know my BFF doesn't like it when I _____ _____

QUESTIONS FOR FRIEND B

1. You know I'm angry when I _____

2. My heart melts immediately when I see _____

3. You could not pay me enough money to go to _____

4. I would give away my most prized possession to go to _____

5. I feel supercool when I am wearing my_____

6. The person who makes me laugh the hardest is _____

7. If I could be any person on the planet I would be _____

8. Sometimes I feel insecure about _____

9. I work very hard to be a good _____

10. My BFF knows better than to talk to me about _____

Scoring:

0-3 Matches: *Worlds Apart*

You call yourselves BFFs? A best friend can sense how you're feeling without being told. You may talk a lot but are you really listening and digesting what the other is saying? Start paying closer attention to each other's words and body language and soon you'll know what the other is thinking without ever saying a word.

4-7 Matches: *On the Right Track*

Great job! You guys are definitely on the same wavelength. Each of you knows what makes the other tick but still maintains the unique qualities that drew you together in the first place.

8-10 Matches: *Soul Sisters*

Wow! Were you two separated at birth? It's like you can read each other's minds! Together you two are a force to be reckoned with. Just be sure to use your conjoined powers for good and not evil.

Our Top Tens _____

year

The best of the year according to YOU!
Use these pages to remember the music,
moments, and more that made this year special.

Favorite Books

1. _____
2. _____
3. _____
4. _____
5. _____
6. _____
7. _____
8. _____
9. _____
10. _____

Coolest Video Games

1. _____
2. _____
3. _____
4. _____
5. _____
6. _____
7. _____
8. _____
9. _____
10. _____

Most Embarrassing Moments

1. _____
2. _____
3. _____
4. _____
5. _____
6. _____
7. _____
8. _____
9. _____
10. _____

Funniest Sayings

1. _____
2. _____
3. _____
4. _____
5. _____
6. _____
7. _____
8. _____
9. _____
10. _____

Cutest Animals

1. _____
2. _____
3. _____
4. _____
5. _____
6. _____
7. _____
8. _____
9. _____
10. _____

Celebrity Crushes

1. _____
2. _____
3. _____
4. _____
5. _____
6. _____
7. _____
8. _____
9. _____
10. _____

Most-Played Songs

1. _____
2. _____
3. _____
4. _____
5. _____
6. _____
7. _____
8. _____
9. _____
10. _____

Best Rainy-Day Activities

1. _____
2. _____
3. _____
4. _____
5. _____
6. _____
7. _____
8. _____
9. _____
10. _____

DIY Friendship Jewelry

Cool accessories to give your BFF or to make together!

Celtic Heart Knot Necklace or Bracelet

You Will Need:

Any of the following: two colors of
regular string, leather string, hoodie string, or thin rope

Instructions:

1. Form a loop with the string.
    The end of the cord, at the right,
    is called the running end.

2. Insert the running end from the
    back through the loop to
    the front.

3. Curve the running end alongside
    itself to form a U-shape, creating
    a second loop. Thread the running
    end into the top loop and out
    through the lower loop.

4. Thread the running end over and under the lower edge of the bottom loop.

5. Continue to loop the running end from front to back in the next loop and from back to front at a diagonal.

6. Adjust the knot until shape is aligned and firm.

FeLT LiNK BRACeLeT

You Will Need:

- Scraps of brightly colored felt
- Thread
- Needle
- Snap fastener
- Scissors

Instructions:

1. Decide which colors your bracelet will be and cut the scraps into small squares and rectangles of similar width.

2. Arrange the pieces in the order you want.

3. Start by placing two pieces next to each other and sewing their edges together. Continue stitching along the outside of one piece until you reach the opposite end. Then repeat this, so you keep adding new pieces and stitching along alternate sides of the bracelet until you've added enough pieces to make the bracelet the length you need.

4. Make your bracelet as long or as short as you want. You may want it to wrap around your arm several times, or keep it short and simple.

5. To finish, sew one half of a small snap fastener to one end of the bracelet, then wrap it around your wrist to see where to sew the matching half. Remove the bracelet from your wrist and sew the second half of the snap in place.

20 BFF PHOTO IDEAS

Tired of duck-face selfies? Try something new! You'll need a tripod or three+ people for some of them.

1. Dress up like tourists and pose in front of local landmarks.

2. Lie head to head on the grass. Have a third person shape your hair into hearts.

3. Re-create famous paintings.

4. Pose for your presidential portrait.

5. Create the cover for your autobiography.

6. Buy some helium balloons and frolic outside.

7. Pretend you're shooting a sneaker advertisement.

8. Re-create a baby picture.

9. Spell out letters with your bodies.

10. Draw scenes on the pavement with chalk and pose with them.

11. Shoot a high-fashion magazine editorial.

12. Use a film camera instead of digital.

13. Create an album cover.

14. Ask someone to braid your hair together.

15. Make a hand heart.

16. Use the black-and-white setting on your photo software.

17. Play on the swings.

18. Leap in the air (try to keep your mouth closed—it's harder than you think).

19. Take a picture of the two of you. Next year, take a picture in the same place holding the photo from the year before. Repeat every year.

20. Do a fancy gymnastics pose.

Quiz: Rate Your Self-Esteem

It's great to have a best friend, but are you a best friend *to yourself*? Take this quiz to find out!

1. Auditions are coming up for the school play. You

   a) sign up right away. You love performing.
   b) are too shy to sign up.
   c) are nervous, but sign up anyway. You like to confront your fears.
   d) check the sign-up board to see who else has signed up. You're not going to compete with someone you think is more likely to win the part.

2. If someone doesn't reply to your message within 24 hours you

   a) worry you've done something to make them mad at you.
   b) assume they're busy.
   c) are angry that they didn't make getting back to you a priority.
   d) keep messaging until they answer.

3. When you have a crush on someone, you

   a) keep it to yourself. Why would that person like me?
   b) assume they'll like you back—who wouldn't?

4. You get a disappointing grade on a book report. You

   a) worry you're stupid.
   b) talk to the teacher to find out where you went wrong.
   c) shrug it off—nobody's perfect.

5. You're thinking of throwing a Halloween party.

a) You decide against it—what if no one comes?
b) go for it! Even if it's just you and your closest pals you'll still have fun!
c) see if anyone else is having one, then plan to outdo it.

6. When the school bus pulls up to your house in the morning, you are most likely

a) giving yourself a final once-over in the mirror.
b) still trying on and rejecting different outfits.
c) ready to go—you're the roll-out-of-bed-and-go type.

7. You see the popular girls whispering in the corner. You

a) ignore them. They're so immature.
b) assume they're whispering about you.
c) are usually the one doing the whispering.

8. When your lunch buddy is away, you

a) head down to the lunchroom and ask to join another group.
b) skip lunch—what if you have to stand there awkwardly and no one invites you to join them?
c) eat by yourself.
d) start networking before lunch to secure a spot with someone else.

9. Dancing in public is

a) your worst nightmare.
b) an opportunity to show off your moves.
c) fun!
d) slightly embarrassing—you don't have the smoothest moves.

Add up your answers:

1. a) 4 b) 1 c) 3 d) 2   4. a) 1 b) 2 c) 3   7. a) 3 b) 1 c) 2
2. a) 1 b) 4 c) 2 d) 2   5. a) 1 b) 3 c) 2   8. a) 4 b) 0 c) 3 d) 2
3. a) 0 b) 2   6. a) 2 b) 1 c) 3   9. a) 1 b) 5 c) 4 d) 2

Scoring:

1-10
Self-esteem Status: *CODE RED*

Uh-oh, someone needs a pep talk! It's natural to be
self-critical, but you may be going overboard. There are
strategies you can learn to shut off the bully in your brain. Talk
to an adult you feel comfortable with, or do some research on
building self-esteem on your own. Your future self will thank you.

11-20
Self-esteem Status: *HEALTHY*

Way to go! You're secure in your own skin and confident in
your abilities. You don't waste time worrying about what
other people might think or say. You see challenges
rather than obstacles and do what you need to do to get
past them. Your future is wide open. The world is yours!

21-30
Self-esteem Status: *PROCEED WITH CAUTION*

Confidence is one thing, but when it verges on arrogance,
things can get ugly fast. It's great that you think you're the jam,
but what's greater and what will get you further in life is to stay
humble despite your high degree of awesomeness. Be your
best, but don't be a show-off.

Totally Tasty Hang-Out Snacks

FRUIT PiZZA

(Adult supervision required)

You Will Need:

- 1 package of refrigerated slice-and-bake sugar cookies OR a premade package of shortbread or sugar cookies

- 1 8-ounce package of cream cheese, softened

- $\frac{1}{2}$ cup powdered sugar

- 1 teaspoon vanilla

- 1 $\frac{1}{2}$ teaspoons lemon juice

- Fresh fruit of choice

Instructions:

1. Follow instructions to make regular-size cookies for "pizza" rounds.

2. To make the topping, mix together cream cheese and powdered sugar until smooth. Stir in the vanilla and lemon juice and set aside until ready to use.

3. Wash and dry fruit. Cut larger fruit like strawberries and kiwis into bite-size pieces. Put out in separate bowls.

4. Spread cream cheese over pizza base and place fruit on top to create fruit pizzas!

HEALTHY GUMMY BEARS

(Adult supervision required)

Helpful Hints:

Freshly squeezed juices are best.

If you can't find a tiny bear cutter in a baking supply store, try the clay mold area of a craft store or look on the Internet.

Whatever flavor you make, instructions #2-8 are exactly the same.

STRAWBERRY-ORANGE GUMMY BEARS

You Will Need:

- ¹/₂ cup orange juice

- ¹/₄ cup lemon juice

- ¹/₄ cup lime juice

- 2 cups strawberries, diced

- 1 packet of zero-calorie natural sweetener

- 5 packets of gelatin

- 1 cookie sheet (the thickness of your pan should be determined by how thick you want your gummies to be)

- Bear cookie cutter or cookie cutter of your choice

Instructions:

1. Combine lemon juice, lime juice, orange juice, and strawberries in a small pot.

2. Bring to a boil, then reduce heat and simmer until fruit is extra soft.

3. Remove mixture from stove and add to a blender or food processor. Add one packet of natural sweetener and blend until smooth.

4. Let the hot mixture cool five to seven minutes.

5. When mixture has cooled, add five packets of gelatin to the blender and blend until there are no clumps.

6. Pour onto a flat baking sheet or tin.

7. Place sheet level in the refrigerator for one hour to firm. Leave in longer if still gooey.

8. When cooled and firmed, remove sheet from the refrigerator and cut out gummies.

Now they're ready to eat!

BLUEBERRY-GRAPEFRUIT GUMMY BEARS

You Will Need:

- Juice from half a grapefruit

- 2 servings of mangosteen juice

- ¼ cup lemon juice

- 2 cups blueberries

- 1 packet of natural sweetener

Instructions:

1. Combine grapefruit juice, mangosteen juice, lemon juice, and blueberries in a small pot.

2. Follow first recipe steps 2 through 8.

BANANA GUMMY BEARS

You Will Need:

- 1 large banana, sliced

- ¼ cup lemon juice

- 1 packet of natural sweetener

Instructions:

1. Mash bananas lightly and combine with lemon juice in a small pot.

2. Follow first recipe steps 2 through 8.

Now try making your own blend of flavors!

GUMMY BEAR POPSICLES

You Will Need:

- Popsicle mold

- Popsicle sticks

- Gummy bears

- Lemon-Lime soda

Instructions:

1. Fill molds about three-quarters of the way full with Lemon-Lime soda.

2. Drop in gummy bears.

3. Place Popsicle sticks into mold.

4. Freeze until frozen all the way through.

Quiz: How Adventurous Are You?

Answer **Yes** or **No** to the following questions in the boxes provided:

Have you ever . . .

	BFF A		BFF B	
	Yes	No	Yes	No
1. Swum in the ocean	☐	☐	☐	☐
2. Eaten a snail	☐	☐	☐	☐
3. Ridden a horse	☐	☐	☐	☐
4. Planted a garden	☐	☐	☐	☐
5. Baked a cake from scratch	☐	☐	☐	☐
6. Slept outdoors	☐	☐	☐	☐
7. Performed in a play	☐	☐	☐	☐
8. Seen a shooting star	☐	☐	☐	☐
9. Worn a tutu	☐	☐	☐	☐
10. Held a spider bigger than a quarter	☐	☐	☐	☐
11. Scored the winning point	☐	☐	☐	☐
12. Written a song	☐	☐	☐	☐
13. Sat in a tree house	☐	☐	☐	☐
14. Broken a bone	☐	☐	☐	☐

	BFF A		BFF B	
	Yes	No	Yes	No
15. Visited a different country	☐	☐	☐	☐
16. Put a worm on a fishing hook	☐	☐	☐	☐
17. Gone upside down on a roller coaster	☐	☐	☐	☐
18. Read a book over 500 pages long	☐	☐	☐	☐
19. Written a letter on paper	☐	☐	☐	☐
20. Watched a horror movie	☐	☐	☐	☐
21. Flown on an airplane	☐	☐	☐	☐
22. Jumped on a trampoline	☐	☐	☐	☐
23. Done volunteer work	☐	☐	☐	☐
24. Changed a baby's diaper	☐	☐	☐	☐
25. Entered a talent competition	☐	☐	☐	☐
26. Shopped in a secondhand store	☐	☐	☐	☐
27. Marched in a parade	☐	☐	☐	☐
28. Gone skating	☐	☐	☐	☐
29. Attended a fan convention	☐	☐	☐	☐
30. Played chess	☐	☐	☐	☐

Scoring:

Give yourself one point for every **YES** answer and add up your score.

1-10 Points: *Snoozy Suzy*

Someone needs to live a little! It's possible to play it safe and still try new things. Make a list of goals and try one new thing each day. Feeling overwhelmed? Aim to try one new thing a week, or even once a month. There's no rush, but getting in the habit of overcoming your inhibitions will make life a lot more rewarding—and fun!

11-20 Points: *Well-rounded Wendy*

Congratulations! You understand that good judgment means knowing when to take risks, and when to play it safe. Keep up the good work.

21-30 Points: *Crazy Cathy*

One thing's for certain—you'll never be accused of being boring! Think about your motivations, though—are you doing these things for yourself, or for attention? It's one thing to be brave, but it's downright dangerous to be a daredevil.

BFF MAKEOVERS

Style Inspiration: Not sure which direction to take? Think about characters you like from books and movies, or celebrities you admire. Start a file with photos and ideas. Think Girl Warrior, Bohemian Princess, Goth Glam, Geek Chic, Country Girl, Urban Adventurer—or experiment and come up with your own mix!

Hair: Want a radical change? Buy some hairstyle magazines. Look for styles where the model's hair texture is similar to yours. Cut out your fav picture and show it to your hairdresser. Remember—don't be afraid to experiment with length—it'll grow back! (But do ask your parents' permission before cutting your hair!)

Wardrobe: In a clothing rut? If you're a jeans-and-hoodie girl, change it up with a skirt or dress every now and then. Cotton fabrics with elastic waists can be comfier than jeans! If you're a girlie girl, try an edgier look. Throw some black or camo into the mix. Browse your closet with your BFF and see what kind of new combinations you can come up with. Consider trading items you rarely wear, or inviting more friends over for a full-on clothing swap!

BFF Costume Ideas

LET YOUR BFF LOVE SHOW, EVEN WHEN YOU'RE ALL DRESSED UP!

The Good Witch of the North and the Wicked Witch of the West
C3P-O and R2D2
Elliott and E.T.
Alice and the White Rabbit
Snoopy and Woodstock
Queen Amidala and her decoy
Ariel and Ursula
Rocky and Bullwinkle
Thing 1 and Thing 2
SpongeBob and Patrick
Calvin and Hobbes
Paper Bag Princess and Dragon
Ms. Pac-Man and ghost
Salt and Pepper
Two Peas in a Pod

FOR THREE+ PEOPLE:

The Chipettes
Paper, Rock, Scissors
The March Sisters: Amy, Meg, Jo, Beth
The kids from *The Sound of Music*

Can you think of more?

_____

_____

_____

_____

Quiz: Would You Rather?

Instructions:

Circle the answer you think **your BFF would prefer**. Trade quizzes to verify. Add up your matches to see how you did!

1. Scuba Dive or Parachute
2. Perform in front of a crowd or Write a novel
3. Explore a new city or Lie on the beach
4. Puppy or Kitten
5. Jeans or Dress
6. French fries or Salad
7. Summer or Winter
8. Fall or Spring

9. Curly hair or Straight hair
10. TV or Movie
11. Night Owl or Early Bird
12. Forest or Desert
13. Explore a cave or Climb a mountain
14. Be an actor or Be a director
15. Citrus or Berry
16. Go to a dance or Stay home and read
17. Chocolate or Chips
18. Hot weather or Cold weather

19. Ride a horse or Ride a roller coaster

20. Sneakers or Sandals

21. Shop or Hike

22. Eat at home or Eat at a restaurant

23. Study arts or Study sciences

24. Big family or Small family

25. Make it yourself or Buy it in a store

26. Short hair or Long hair

27. Swim or Snowboard

28. Photographer or Model

29. Bike or Walk

30. Fast food or Fancy dining

31. Makeup or Fresh-faced

32. Pink or Black

33. Jump rope or Skateboard

34. Class clown or Teacher's pet

35. Win a new computer or an exotic vacation

36. Follow a schedule or Play it by ear

37. Romance or Science fiction books

38. Diamond necklace or Baseball cap

39. Video games or Art gallery

40. Camp or Hotel

Quiz: Would You Rather?

Instructions:

Circle the answer you think **your BFF would prefer**. Trade quizzes to verify. Add up your matches to see how you did!

1. Scuba Dive or Parachute
2. Perform in front of a crowd or Write a novel
3. Explore a new city or Lie on the beach
4. Puppy or Kitten
5. Jeans or Dress
6. French fries or Salad
7. Summer or Winter
8. Fall or Spring

9. Curly hair or Straight hair
10. TV or Movie
11. Night Owl or Early Bird
12. Forest or Desert
13. Explore a cave or Climb a mountain
14. Be an actor or Be a director
15. Citrus or Berry
16. Go to a dance or Stay home and read
17. Chocolate or Chips
18. Hot weather or Cold weather

19. Ride a horse or Ride a roller coaster

20. Sneakers or Sandals

21. Shop or Hike

22. Eat at home or Eat at a restaurant

23. Study arts or Study sciences

24. Big family or Small family

25. Make it yourself or Buy it in a store

26. Short hair or Long hair

27. Swim or Snowboard

28. Photographer or Model

29. Bike or Walk

30. Fast food or Fancy dining

31. Makeup or Fresh-faced

32. Pink or Black

33. Jump rope or Skateboard

34. Class clown or Teacher's pet

35. Win a new computer or an exotic vacation

36. Follow a schedule or Play it by ear

37. Romance or Science fiction books

38. Diamond necklace or Baseball cap

39. Video games or Art gallery

40. Camp or Hotel

The Movie of My Life

STARRING:

Title:

_____

Subtitle:

_____

Costarring:

_____

Directed by:

_____

Written by:

_____

Soundtrack featuring:

_____

Costume Design by:

_____

Rated:

_____

Synopsis:

_____

Website: _____.com

Poster:

The Movie of My Life

STARRING:

Title:

_____

Subtitle:

_____

Costarring:

_____

Directed by:

_____

Written by:

_____

Soundtrack featuring:

_____

Costume Design by:

_____

Rated:

_____

Synopsis:

_____

Website: _____.com

Poster:

MAKE IT TOGETHER

Nothing to do on a rainy afternoon? These fun and easy projects will keep you busy.

NO-SEW T-SHIRT PILLOW

You Will Need:

- T-shirt

- Scissors

- Small pillow or stuffing

- Fabric chalk

- Ruler

Instructions:

1. Take an old T-shirt, preferably with writing or a picture on the front. Lay it down on a flat workspace and smooth out the surface.

2. Mark a square with fabric chalk—however big you want your pillow to be. Then mark another square inside of the large square—about 3 inches from the sides and 2 ½ inches from the top and bottom of the shirt.

3. Cut the large square out, careful to cut BOTH the top and bottom layer of the tee. Keep it flat on your work surface.

4. Cut 1-inch indents from the outside of the square to the inside, marked square—all the way around and through both layers. You can cut the corners off.

5. Keeping the two layers together, start tying each top and bottom coordinating 1-inch strip.

6. Tie three sides and then slide an old pillow through the top or fill with stuffing.**

7. Finish tying off the top of the pillow and make sure all ties are secure.

Presto! A fun pillow!

**To make your pillow a pet bed, add slightly less stuffing.

DESIGN YOUR OWN SNEAKERS

You Will Need:

- Plain canvas shoes
- Fabric markers (look for ones with a thick consistency)
- Fabric paint
- Masking tape

You may want to make a rough sketch of your design before starting.

GEOMETRIC DESIGN

Instructions:

1. Remove the laces and mask off a line.

2. Use your fabric marker to create a herringbone pattern. Continue across until the white toe and back heel sections are covered.

3. Paint the middle section with black fabric paint.

All done!

46

RANDOM PATTERN

1. Paint spots, blocks, and shapes all over the canvas parts of the shoes with colorful fabric paint.

2. Add small dots and geometric patterns with black paint to finish.

Care: Let your shoes dry for three or four days before wearing. Follow the washing instructions included with the fabric markers and paints.

No-Sew Socktopus

You Will Need:

- Some fun knee socks
- Felt scraps in three colors (for the eyes)
- Fabric glue
- Polyester or cotton stuffing
- Scissors
- Thread

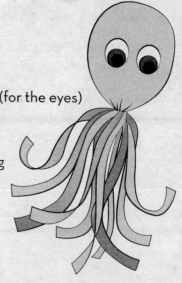

Instructions:

1. Stuff your sock. Two or three handfuls should do it. The more stuffing you add, the more of an oval shape you'll get.

2. Wrap a 12-inch piece of thread several times around the sock right under where the stuffing ends. Knot the thread so that it looks like a sock balloon.

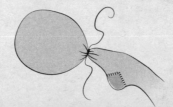

3. Cut the sock off where you want the "tentacles" to end.

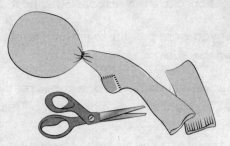

4. Cut eight tentacles.

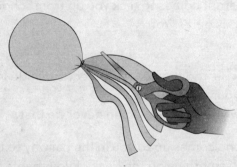

5. Cut two circles from each color of felt. Cut a small set for the pupils, a larger set for the irises, and a slightly larger set for the whites of the eyes. Glue them together with the biggest circle on the bottom, and the smallest on top.

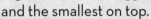

6. Glue the eyes onto your Socktopus. Let them dry.

Ready to love!

Quiz: How Easily Embarrassed Are You?

For each question, circle the response that best describes you.

1. A letter you were passing to a friend is intercepted by a classmate. You

    a) gather your classmates for a public reading.
    b) shriek and lunge for it—it must not be read!
    c) accept your fate.
    d) only send texts so this won't happen.

2. Your parent comes to pick you up from school in a ridiculous outfit. You

    a) laugh.
    b) duck behind the nearest object and hide in shame.
    c) roll your eyes and sigh.
    d) know your parents would never do that.

3. Someone comes up to you in the hallway to tell you there's something on the back of your pants. You

    a) say, "Oh, that—it's supposed to be there!"
    b) gasp, try to twist around to see it and cover it up while scurrying to the bathroom.
    c) thank them.
    d) always check yourself out in any reflective surface so this won't happen.

4. Your teacher calls on you in class but you didn't do your homework, so you

    a) make something up on the fly.
    b) turn bright red and feel tears building.
    c) admit you don't know the answer.
    d) *pfft*. You always do your homework.

5. Accidentally walking into the boy's bathroom, you

 a) make a comment about the fancy new sinks.
 b) shriek in embarrassment and run out.
 c) calmly turn around and walk out.
 d) always double-check the sign before entering.

6. A friend posts an unflattering photo of you online. You

 a) comment that she always knows how to find your best side.
 b) untag yourself and pray your crush doesn't see it.
 c) laugh and forget about it.
 d) demand she remove it immediately.

7. You're celebrating your birthday at a restaurant. A parade of singing servers marches over to your table with a flaming cake. You

 a) love the attention.
 b) slouch down as far as you can in your seat and wait for the misery to end.
 c) smile graciously.
 d) make your friends promise not to tell the restaurant it's your birthday, so this would never happen.

8. You fall in the middle of a dance recital. You

 a) try to keep a straight face.
 b) blink back tears and struggle to hold it together.
 c) pop back up and carry on like nothing happened.
 d) quit dancing. You'll never live that down.

9. In the heat of anger you send someone a mean message and regret it afterward. You

a) vow that in the future you will wait a day before sending any message written in anger.

b) send a stream of panicky messages trying to explain your actions.

c) talk to the recipient in person, explaining you made a mistake and apologize.

d) shrug it off. They deserved it.

Scoring:

Add up how many of each letter you circled.

Mostly As

Thanks to your quick thinking and well-developed sense of humor, you find a way to turn embarrassing moments into opportunities to showcase your wit and intelligence. You don't take yourself too seriously.

Mostly Bs

Hey, it's okay! Stop worrying so much about what other people think of you. They are far too busy worrying about their own behavior to focus on yours.

Mostly Cs

You're a cool cat and not much ruffles your feathers. You accept that embarrassing things happen to everyone and move on as quickly as possible. Your grace in the face of public scrutiny will serve you well in life.

Mostly Ds

How do you spell Control Freak? Y-O-U. How can you enjoy life if you're so busy trying to control it? Ask yourself what's really driving your need to be perfect? Usually it's fear and insecurity. The sooner you deal with the root problem, the better.

GET MOVING!

Spending too much time staring at a screen? Feeling sluggish and lazy? Then grab your BFF and get moving—it's way more fun with company!

OUR WORKOUT PLAYLIST

Before you start your workout, decide together what music will get your heart pumping and your body moving!

Warm-up

_____

_____

_____

_____

_____

Peak Workout

_____

_____

_____

_____

_____

Cool Down

_____

_____

_____

_____

_____

Wall sit

Do the following series of exercises three times a week:

1. *Light aerobics (2–3 min)* Walking, jogging on the spot, and jumping jacks will get your heart pumping and warm up your joints and muscles.

2. *Range of motion movements or active stretches (2–3 min)* Starting with your head and moving downward, do side-side neck rolls, shoulder and arm circles in both directions, trunk twists in both directions, hip circles, leg side-side swings, and standing toe touches. These develop balance and flexibility.

3. *Push-ups from your knees or against a wall* As many as you can without stopping!

4. *Body squats (1–2 min)* Feet shoulder-width apart, hands on your hips, lower your body as if you're sitting in a chair behind you. Repeat this without bending your knees more than 90 degrees.

5. *Stomach crunches (1–2 min)* Lie on your back with your knees bent, feet on the floor, and hands on your thighs. Raise your shoulders off the ground until your hands slide up your legs and cover your knees. Return to starting position and continue.

6. *Wall sit (2 min)* Lean against a wall with your feet shoulder-width apart. Make sure your feet are in line with your knees and not too close to the wall. Slowly lower your body to a sitting position and hold.

7. *Shake your body out, get a sip of water, and repeat steps one through six two more times.*

This program will take anywhere from 15 to 25 minutes. Try this program at least three days a week. Switch the order of exercises often, and substitute exercises with whatever comes to mind.

Not in the mood for regular sports? Here are some fun ways to be active that don't feel like exercise!

Hula-hooping

Miniature golf

Bowling

Indoor rock-climbing

Roller derby

Obstacle courses

Building a snowman

Sledding

Walking and playing fetch with your dog (or a borrowed one)

Frisbee

Kite flying

Dancing

Parkour

Quiz: Best Friends 4Ever?

Sure, you're best buds now, but will you still be friends when you're old and gray?

1. Your BFF got the highest grade in the class on your last English test, so you

   a) give her a high five.
   b) feel envious and wish you could do well, too.
   c) say nothing and seethe with jealousy.

2. You're inviting your classmates to your birthday party. Your BFF goes to a different school and won't know anybody, so you

   a) don't invite her. You don't want to have to babysit her.
   b) invite her to come early so you can introduce her to each guest as they arrive.
   c) ask her to help out with hosting duties so she feels important and has tasks to do if she feels shy.
   d) just invite her; she'll be fine.

3. You love your BFF's style and are always asking to borrow clothes, which you

   a) wash carefully, fold neatly, and return as soon as possible.
   b) treat like your own, which means leaving them on the floor.
   c) usually forget to give back.

4. You like hanging out with your BFF because

a) you feel smarter and prettier in comparison.
b) you can 100 percent be yourself in her company.
c) she's supercool and you hope some of it rubs off on you.

5. You and your BFF argue

a) all the time.
b) rarely, but it happens.
c) never. No one argues with me.
d) Not very often. It's not worth rocking the boat.

6. A friend invites you to an event that you'd love to attend. Unfortunately, it falls on the same night you and your BFF have a sleepover planned. You

a) call your BFF and make an excuse as to why you can't make it.
b) ask if your BFF can come, too.
c) tell your BFF the truth and ask if she would mind rescheduling for another night.
d) turn down the invitation. You already have plans.

7. When it comes to your BFF, your family

a) thinks she's great! She's part of the family.
b) has never met her.
c) is unsure—they've never said anything.
d) doesn't like her.

8. If your BFF didn't hear from you for two days she would

a) freak out. She gets alarmed when she doesn't hear from you every few hours.
b) probably not notice.
c) leave some messages expressing concern.

9. Your BFF has been spending a lot of time lately with another friend. You

a) feel jealous.
b) don't mind.
c) wish they would invite you along, too.

10. Your BFF's birthday is coming up. You

a) plan to grab a gift at the last minute.
b) have the PERFECT gift. You can't wait for her to open it.
c) aren't sure what to get her, so you pick out something that you'd like to receive.

Scoring:

1. A+10/B+5/C+3
2. A+1/B+10/C+8/D+5
3. A+9/B+7/C+2
4. A+1/B+10/C+6
5. A+1/B+5/C+3/D+2
6. A+1/B+4/C+7/D+10
7. A+8/B+4/C+5/D+2
8. A+6/B+3/C+8
9. A+3/B+8/C+5
10. A+3/B+8/C+3

Add up your points to find out if you're really best friends forever.

1-20 Points: All signs point to NO. Did your friendship even survive the reading of this book? If a friendship is making you feel sad more than it's making you feel happy, it's time to seriously consider pulling the plug.

21-40 Points: The odds are NOT in your favor. Friends come and go throughout life. Sometimes you're brought together through a shared experience like school or a hobby and once that experience is over there's not much left to bond over. This is natural, so keep in mind that all best friends aren't necessarily forever.

41-62 Points: There's a good chance you'll make it. You may not always be as close as you are now, but your strong bond means your lives will likely stay connected in some way.

63-86 Points: BFFs 4ever and ever! No matter how far apart life takes you, you know you'll see each other again and when you do it will feel like no time has passed at all. You two are the definition of "Friends till the End."

My Predictions for the Future

Think about all of your friends and the awesome things they'll be doing in the future. Then compare answers with your BFF!

By _____, at _____,
   your name   *your location*

on _____, in _____.
   this day of month   *the year*

Friend most likely to be valedictorian: _____

Friend most likely to star in a Broadway play: _____

Friend most likely to win an Olympic medal: _____

Friend most likely to cure cancer: _____

Friend most likely to be the next J.K. Rowling: _____

Friend most likely to become a princess: _____

Friend most likely to record a number one hit song:
_____

Friend most likely to live on a farm: _____

Friend most likely to become president: _____

My Predictions for the Future

Think about all of your friends and the awesome things they'll be doing in the future. Then compare answers with your BFF!

By _____, at _____,
        your name   *your location*

on _____, in _____.
        this day of month   *the year*

Friend most likely to be valedictorian: _____

Friend most likely to star in a Broadway play: _____

Friend most likely to win an Olympic medal: _____

Friend most likely to cure cancer: _____

Friend most likely to be the next J.K. Rowling: _____

Friend most likely to become a princess: _____

Friend most likely to record a number one hit song:
_____

Friend most likely to live on a farm: _____

Friend most likely to become president: _____

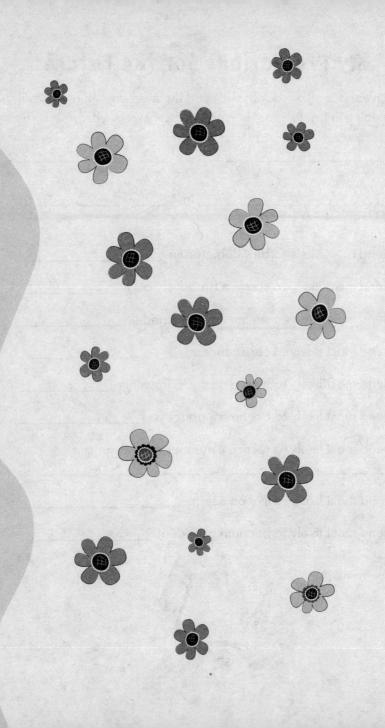